TORTILLAS are ROUND

Las tortillas son redondas

To Maya, a true tortilla fan, and to friends old and new, who love large, round, floppy, flappy, slightly singed, just-off-the-stovetop tortillas —R. G. T.

To my aunts Irma, Amelia, Adela, Gloria, Julia, Yolanda, and Grace, for all those wonderful winter tamales and summer barbeque memories —J. P.

A Maya, una verdadera amante de las tortillas, y a los viejos y nuevos amigos a los que les gustan las tortillas grandes, redondas, suaves, un poco chamuscadas y recién sacadas del sartén —R. G. T.

A mis tías Irma, Amelia, Adela, Gloria, Julia, Yolanda y Grace, por todos esos recuerdos maravillosos de tamales en el invierno y barbacoas en el verano —J. P.

Originally published in English as *Round Is a Tortilla* by Chronicle Books LLC.

ISBN 978-0-545-70925-5

12 11 10 9 8 7 6 5 4 3 2 1 14 15 16 17 18 19/0

Printed in the U.S.A. 40
First Scholastic bilingual printing, September 2014

Book design by Eloise Leigh.
Typeset in Brandon Grotesque.
The illustrations in this book were rendered in paint.

TORTILLAS are ROUND

Las tortillas son redondas

A Book of Shapes

Un libro de figuras geométricas

Roseanne Greenfield Thong

Illustrated by / *Ilustrado por* John Parra

SCHOLASTIC INC.

Round are *sombreros*.
Round is the moon.
Round are the trumpets
that blare out a tune.

Redondos son los sombreros.
Redonda es la luna.
Redondas son las trompetas
que tocan una canción.

Round are *campanas*
that chime and ring.

Redondas son las campanas
que repican y llaman.

Round are the nests
where swallows sing.

*Redondos son los nidos
en los que cantan
las golondrinas.*

Round are *tortillas* and *tacos*, too.
Round is a pot of *abuela's* stew.
I can name more round things. Can you?

Redondas son las tortillas y los tacos también.
Redonda es la olla para el pozole de la abuela.
Puedo nombrar más cosas redondas.
¿Puedes tú?

Square are the letters—we know them well.
Square is a board game to help us spell.

Cuadradas son las letras que tan bien conocemos.
Cuadrado es un juego que nos ayuda a deletrear.

plaza
cuadrad
suenos
A1

Square are *ventanas*
that give a view.
Square is my clock,
and my photos, too.

Cuadradas son las ventanas
que muestran el paisaje.
Cuadrado es mi reloj
y mis fotos también.

Square is the park, and the *zócalo*.
Square is a fountain from long ago.
How many square things do you know?

Cuadrados son el parque y el zócalo.
Cuadrada es una fuente muy vieja.
¿Cuántas cosas cuadradas conoces?

Rectangles are carts
with bells that chime
and cold *paletas*
in summertime.

Rectangulares son los carritos
con campanas que repican
y paletas frías
en el verano.

Muy Frío
Muy Delicioso
PALETAS

Stone *metates* inside our *casa*
help us grind our corn to *masa*.

También los metates de piedra de nuestra casa
que nos ayudan a moler el maíz para hacer la masa.

Rectangles are flags that fly above the scoreboard, way up high. How many rectangles do you spy?

Rectangulares son las banderas que ondean en lo alto. ¿Cuántas cosas rectangulares puedes ver?

SAN LUIS REY
MISSIONS
1 2 3 4 5 6 7 8 9 Total
Guest 1 0 0 2 0 0 2 5
Home 2 3 0 4 0 0 3 12

Triangles are crunchy chips
for *guacamole* and other dips.

Triangulares son los totopos crujientes
para el guacamole y otras salsas.

Triangles sail on the breeze.
They line the shore and glide on seas.

Y triangulares son las velas que se inflan con la brisa.
Bordean la orilla y por los mares navegan.

Sandías chilled in tubs of ice,
quesadillas by the slice—
triangles can beat the heat.
What other triangles can you eat?

Triangulares son los pedazos de sandía sobre el hielo
y también las porciones de quesadilla...
Alimentos que nos refrescan cuando hace calor.
¿Qué otras cosas triangulares puedes comer?

Oval is my favorite locket,
a special pebble in my pocket.

I find ovals at the store,
huevos, olives, beans galore.
Can you name a couple more?

Ovalado es mi medallón favorito,
y una piedrita especial que llevo en el bolsillo.

Veo cosas ovaladas en el mercado:
huevos, aceitunas y muchos frijoles.
¿Puedes nombrar dos cosas más?

FRESCO
LECHE

Stars for parties, stars for light,
lining streets with colors bright.
There are so many shapes wherever you go.
How many more shapes do you know?

Estrellas para las fiestas, estrellas que dan luz,
dispuestas en las calles con colores brillantes.
Hay figuras geométricas por dondequiera que vas.
¿Cuántas más conoces?

GLOSSARY

Guacamole: A dip made with avocado, onion, tomato, chili pepper, and seasoning.

Mariachis: A musical group that plays a form of Mexican folk music called Mariachi.

Masa: Corn flour used for Mexican foods like *tamales* (packets of filled, steamed dough) and *tortillas*.

Metate: A flat or slightly hollowed piece of rock, used with a stone rolling pin called *mano*.

Paleta: A frozen-fruit bar.

Pozole: A Mexican stew made with large kernels of corn soaked in lime water and dried, and often containing pork, chili, seasonings, and vegetables.

Quesadilla: A *tortilla* folded over a filling of hot, melted cheese.

Taco: A *tortilla*, sometimes folded, sometimes flat, piled with fillings and served hot.

Tortillas: Round, flatbread pancakes made from *masa* (corn flour dough) or wheat, and baked on a hot surface. (In Spain, *tortillas* are thick egg omelets fried with potatoes.)

Zócalo: Every town and city in Mexico has a *zócalo* or main square, often filled with shady trees, gardens, benches, and fountains. People young and old gather to chat, rest, look at artwork, and listen to bands and entertainers.